Elizabeth's Tuition Centre

Bond

10 Minute Tests

10-11 years

Frances Down

Verbal Reasoning

™Nelson Thornes
a Wolters Kluwer business

TEST 1: Similars and Opposites

Underline the two words, one from each group, which are closest in meaning.

Example: (brother, <u>friend</u>, animal)   (family, horse, <u>chum</u>)

1   (<u>bus</u>, driver, pedestrian)   (zebra crossing, <u>car</u>, traffic lights)
2   (write, <u>explain</u>, shout)   (sleep, <u>weep</u>, cry)
3   (swallowed, ~~bitten~~, eaten)   (<u>gnawed</u>, torn, gorged)
4   (yellow, <u>pink</u>, path)   (dandelion, <u>rose</u>, garden)

Underline the two words, one from each group, which are the most opposite in meaning.

Example: (dawn, <u>early</u>, wake)   (<u>late</u>, stop, sunrise)

5   (<u>tidy</u>, dust, clean)   (neat, <u>scruffy</u>, brush)
6   (climb, <u>broad</u>, slender)   (<u>narrow</u>, wide, high)
7   (hearty, cough, <u>unwell</u>)   (strong, cold, <u>healthy</u>)
8   (<u>pale</u>, red, coloured)   (<u>flushed</u>, faint, whiten)

Give a word that is similar in meaning to the word in capital letters and that rhymes with the second word.

Example: BATTLE   sight   <u>FIGHT</u>

9   DEFEND   detect   _____
10   LOOSE   black   _____
11   SPRINT   lace   _____
12   SLICE   fleece   _____
13   KNOT   sigh   _____
14   MINUTE   shiny   _____

Underline the one word in brackets which will go equally well with both pairs of words outside the brackets.

Example: world, planet   soil, ground   (night, space, <u>earth</u>, sphere)

15   talon, pincer   scratch, tear   (rake, nail, foot, <u>claw</u>)
16   even, flat   position, stage   (<u>level</u>, dull, horizontal, period)
17   pour, empty out   end, furthest point   (overbalance, apex, <u>tip</u>, fall)
18   site, situation   put, allocate   (location, <u>place</u>, circumstance, move)
19   clean, clear   innocent, virtuous   (<u>pure</u>, not guilty, harmless, hygienic)
20   remain, stay   linger, delay   (serve, continue, <u>wait</u>, endure)

Total [   ]

Write the four-letter word hidden at the end of one word and the beginning of the next word. The order of the letters may not be changed.

Example: He liked fish and chips.   hand

1   Please attach the labels to your jackets.   _Seat_

2   The match is hanging in the balance.   _____

3   It is a good thing we are firm friends.   _____

4   My sister makes me tidy my room.   ___ℓ___

5   The tramp had bare stumps rather than teeth.   _____

6   Cutting my finger made me cry.   _____

7   The team made errors to lose the cricket match.   _____

8   I had to do my homework all over again.   _____

9   Joe said the blue bike was his.   _____

10   My cat gave birth in September to five kittens.   _____

11   His right ankle was broken when he fell off his bike.   _tank_

12   Brian's thumb and forefinger were bruised by the fall.   _____

13   Mary made a crucial catch at the start of the contest.   _____

14   Darkness fell and Sarah could not see the path.   _____

15   Which do you prefer, this zebra or that elephant?   _____

16   A long icicle appeared on her window sill last night.   _____

17   The ghostly sound of each owl could be heard.   _____

18   My cousins have stones all round their pond.   _____

19   In an airport lounge any unattended parcel looks suspicious.   _____

20   Pour the cream into the striped jug please.   _____

Total

TEST 3: **Substitution**

If A=1, B=2, C=3 and so on, write the values of the following words if the letters are added together.

Example: ADDED   <u>18</u>   (1+4+4+5+4=18)

1   FADE   _____

2   BACK   _____

3   HIGH   _____

4   BALL   _____

If p=10, q=4, r=3, s=6, t=2 and u=24, find the value of the following.

5   $(p + r) - s =$ _____

6   $ps =$ _____

7   $(\frac{u}{q}) \times s =$ _____

8   $(u - p) + (s - q) =$ _____

Using the same values as above, write the answers as letters.

9   $(u - q) - p =$ _____

10   $qrt =$ _____

11   $pr - s =$ _____

12   $q^2 - p =$ _____

13   $\frac{qs}{u} + t =$ _____

14   $\frac{s+u}{p} =$ _____

If A=1, E=2, L=3, P=4, S=5 and T=6, find the values of these words when the letters are added together.

15   PLEASE   _____

16   STEEL   _____

17   PLEAT   _____

18   LEAST   _____

19   STAPLE   _____

Using the same values as above, work out the value of this calculation.

20   LAPSE – PALE   _____

4

Total

Tom had six lessons in different classrooms. Match the lessons he studied with the six unshaded rooms.

Tom studied English in a classroom with a lower number than the one he used for French.

History was in the classroom, directly across the corridor, opposite the classroom for Geography.

Maths was in between and next door to Geography and Science.

Science 5	*Maths* 4	*Geograhy* 3	2	*English* 1

C O R R I D O R

10	9	8	7	6

History   *French*

1–6 Room 1 = _____   Room 3 = _____   Room 4 = _____

Room 5 = _____   Room 7 = _____   Room 8 = _____

From the information supplied, answer the questions.

An explorer was in a dilemma. He needed to travel north-west to his camp. In between was a large crocodile infested swamp. If he travelled north and then west, he had to go over a mountain range. If he travelled west and then north, he would encounter a fierce tribe of natives.

What would the explorer encounter:

7   south of the camp? _____   **8**   east of the camp? _____

In which direction would the explorer have to start to go if he decided to:

9   go over the mountains towards the camp?   _____

10   go past the fierce tribe towards the camp?   _____

11   go through the swamp towards the camp?   _____

Class 6S were collecting information to make a graph on the pets owned by the class.

Rabbits were owned by Darren, William, Sita, Jane and Phil.
Sita, Brett, Jane and Sven all had goldfish. All those who owned a goldfish also had a cat, except Sven. William and Darren also had a dog.
Sandy, William and Brett each had a gerbil. Phil and Sita had a tortoise.

12   How many types of pets are mentioned?   _____

13–14 What pets does Darren have?   _____ _____

15   How many children are mentioned?   _____

16–17 Which two children only have one pet each?   _____ _____

18   Who has a dog and a gerbil?   _____

19   Who has a cat and a gerbil?   _____

20   Who has the most pets?   _____

Total _____

Find the letter that will end the first word and start the second word.

Example: FAS T RACK

1 ORANG __ VERY

2 SHEL __ IMP

3 SILL __ OLK

4 PINC __ OVEL

5 PEAR __ AUGH

6 MAS __ PENT

Move one letter from the first word to the second word to make two new words.

	Example: BREAD	COW	BEAD	CROW
7	CHASE	CAP	_____	_____
8	CRUDE	ARE	_____	_____
9	BREAD	TINT	_____	_____
10	BUNG	AMBLE	_____	_____
11	WANT	PIN	_____	_____
12	BRIDLE	GROWING	_____	_____
13	WHINE	HEART	_____	_____

The middle word in the first group has been made by taking two letters from the other two words. Complete the second group of three words in the same way, making a new word in the middle of the second group.

	Example: PAIN	INTO	TOOK	ALSO	SOON	ONLY
14	PAST	STOP	OPEN	SOON	_____	TOWN
15	HOOP	OPEN	THEN	PILE	_____	DAFT
16	GRIN	GRIP	PINK	PLUG	_____	NAVE
17	TIME	MILK	LOOK	SLED	_____	SORE
18	PAST	SPOT	TORN	ROTA	_____	YAWN
19	DUMB	BULB	LOBE	LAWN	_____	VEER
20	RAFT	FIRM	MIRE	CALM	_____	FOAM

Total

TEST 6: **Word Progressions 2**

Change the first word into the last word by changing one letter at a time and making a new, different word in the middle.

Example: CASE   CASH   LASH

1	FARM	_____	HARK
2	RULE	_____	SOLE
3	PARK	_____	PANT
4	TONE	_____	TUNA
5	BELL	_____	MELT
6	TICK	_____	SINK
7	CANE	_____	CURE

Change the first word into the last word by changing one letter at a time, and making two new, different words in the middle.

Example: FLIP   SLIP   SLIM   SWIM

8	TYPE	_____	_____	CASE
9	SORT	_____	_____	FIRM
10	DIET	_____	_____	PANT
11	TIME	_____	_____	SAFE
12	BOWL	_____	_____	FOAM
13	FIND	_____	_____	VANE
14	PAIR	_____	_____	DAWN
15	LIME	_____	_____	LAZY
16	PAST	_____	_____	FISH
17	PINK	_____	_____	SAND
18	GOAT	_____	_____	BEAN
19	DEER	_____	_____	LEAF
20	BONE	_____	_____	BARK

Total

The code for the word COMPUTER is 72384169. Encode each of these words using the same code.

1   TRUE   _____

2   RUMP   _____

Decode these words using the same code as above.

3   3296   _____

4   8291   _____

If the code for SPENT is ORJAZ, what word is:

5   AJOZ   _____

6   OZJR   _____

If the code for CALMER is $+x£-@, what would be the code for:

7   MALE   _____

8   RACE   _____

Match the right word to each code given below.
TEST   MAST   TAME   STEM

9   4617   _____   **11**   3471   _____

10   4734   _____   **12**   1634   _____

Decode these words using the same code as above.

13   7634   _____   **14**   1764   _____

Here are the codes for four words.
9mQ%   mX%3   3Xm9   %Qm9
Match the right code to each word.

15   TURN   _____

16   RATS   _____

17   STAR   _____

18   NUTS   _____

Encode these words using the same code as above.

19   STUNT   _____

20   SATURN   _____

Total _____

A B C D E F G H I J K L M N O P Q R S T U V W X Y Z

The word FOOTBALL is written in a code as GPPUCBMM.
Using the same code:

1 encode the word SOCCER _____

2 decode HPBM _____

The word TYPE is written in code as VARG. Encode these words using the same code.

3 JAM _____

4 ZEBRA _____

The word FAST is written in code as CXPQ. Encode these words using the same code.

5 TABLE _____

6 PINK _____

Decode these words using the same code as above.

7 MXOQ _____

8 GXAB _____

The word BEAD is written in code as 2514. Encode these words using the same code.

9 FEED _____

10 CAGE _____

11 HEAD _____

Decode these words using the same code as above.

12 6135 _____

13 85475 _____

14 If the code for RIGHT is WNLMY, what is the code for LEFT? _____

The code for the word BLACK is eodfn. Using the same code, pick the correct codes for these words.
sodq   odun   edun   sodb

15 BARK _____   **17** LARK _____

16 PLAY _____   **18** PLAN _____

Decode these words using the same code as above.

19 elug _____   **20** iohz _____

(9)

Total

Test time: 0 |||||||||| 10 minutes

A B C D E F G H I J K L M N O P Q R S T U V W X Y Z

Give the missing groups of letters or numbers in each sequence.

Example:	A3	B4	C5	<u>D6</u>	<u>E7</u>			
1	3	6	9	12	___	___		
2	10	4	20	6	___	___		
3	AA	CC	EE	GG	___	___		
4	Ab	Cd	Ef	Gh	___			
5	79	72	65	58	___	___		
6	33	zz	22	yy	___	___		
7	15m	18p	21s	24v	___			
8	___	17	19	___	23	25		
9	WU	VS	___	TO	___	RK		
10	___	___	8	16	32	64		
11	___	P23	___	L43	J53	H63		
12	6	___	12	8	___	12	24	16
13	___	2	4	___	6	8	8	16
14	a3Z	b5Y	___	___	e11V	f13U	g15T	h17S
15	2	5	9	14	___	___	35	44
16	3	17	6	15	___	13	12	___
17	___	___	16	15	20	18	24	21
18	AB	DC	___	HG	IJ	___	MN	PO
19	3Z	___	6X	___	13V	18U	24T	31S
20	AZ	BY	___	___	EV	FU	GT	HS

Total

Test time: 0 | | | | | 5 | | | | | 10 minutes

A B C D E F G H I J K L M N O P Q R S T U V W X Y Z

Give the missing groups of letters in each sequence.

Example: AB is to CD as PQ is to <u>RS</u>

1   FG is to JK as LM is to _____

2   RO is to NK as JG is to _____

3   aF is to gL as mR is to _____

4   PON is to MLK as JIH is to _____

5   FD is to HF as JH is to _____

6   Ah is to Dk as Gn is to _____

7   DcE is to FeG as HgI is to _____

8   VL is to TJ as RH is to _____

9   ZA is to YB as XC is to _____

10   aCe is to fHj as kMo is to _____

Give the missing groups of letters or numbers in each sequence.

11   16 is to 19 as 24 is to _____

12   13a is to 14b as 15c is to _____

13   Z11 is to X10 as V9 is to _____

14   A*D is to E*H as I*L is to _____

15   M12N is to O14P as Q16R is to _____

16   77 is to 55 as 44 is to _____

17   aZ is to bY as cX is to _____

18   NMK is to JIG as HGE is to _____

19   AF is to CH as EJ is to _____

20   ?90! is to !80? as ?70! is to _____

Total

Look at these groups of words.

A	B	C	D	E
rugby	iron	eagle	scarlet	rain
netball	lead	penguin	orange	cloud

Choose the correct group for each of these words below. Write in the group letter.

1–5 steel _____   flamingo _____   hail _____

purple _____   azure _____   hockey _____

sun _____   seagull _____   platinum _____

football _____

Find the two letters that will end the first word and start the second word.

Example: FRU _IT_   EM

6   CLA _____   OON   **9**   VARNI _____   OUT

7   SWIV _____   ECT   **10** PAN _____   ICLE

8   STY _____   MON

Take away one letter from the word in capital letters to make a new word.
The meaning of the new word is given in the clue.

Example: SPEED   you plant it   <u>SEED</u>

11 TABLE   a story '   _____

12 CLIMB   an arm or a leg   _____

13 BRIDLE   marries a groom   _____

14 FOWL   a night bird   _____

15 STEEP   a pace   _____

Underline the two words that are the odd ones out in each group of words.

Example: (house, office, <u>tractor</u>, bungalow, <u>chimney</u>)

16 (boot, door, slipper, car, snowshoe)

17 (beetroot, carrot, peach, apple, clementine)

18 (bear, camel, salmon, crocodile, mouse)

19 (camera, CD player, radio, tape recorder, binoculars)

20 (forest, lake, orchard, pond, wood)

Total

Underline the two words, one from each group, which are closest in meaning.

Example: (brother, <u>friend</u>, animal)   (family, horse, <u>chum</u>)

1   (appear, disappear, collapse)   (vanish, rebuild, apply)

2   (competent, competitor, companion)   (capable, enemy, canopy)

3   (blue, aquamarine, scarlet)   (black, beige, crimson)

4   (scamper, run, skip)   (hop, scurry, scrounge)

5   (rubbish, wasteful, skip)   (dust, wasteland, uneconomical)

Write the four-letter word hidden at the end of one word and the beginning of the next word. The order of the letters may not be changed.

Example: He liked fi<u>sh and</u> chips.   <u>hand</u>

6   Please remember you must open each window slowly.   _____

7   I avoided the girl who made me cry.   _____

8   The rope bridge swung in the breeze.   _____

9   Explorers make epic journeys across the globe.   _____

10   Tom's ball dented the wing of his father's car.   _____

From the information supplied, underline the one statement below it that must be true.

11   Butter is a dairy product. Dairy products are made from milk.

   A Butter is made from milk.   **C** Dairy products are yellow.

   B Milk comes from cows.   **D** Cheese is a dairy product.

Find the letter that will end the first word and start the second word.

Example: FAS <u>T</u>   RACK

12   BUIL   ___   ROWN   14   TWIC   ___   NDURE

13   STAM   ___   ROUD   15   DAIS   ___   EARN

If A=5, S=4, T=3, R=2 and E=1, find the values of the following words when the letters are added together.

16   RAT   _____   19   REST   _____

17   EAR   _____   20   STARE   _____

18   STAR   _____

Total [   ]

Here are the number codes for four words.
3256 3526 6225 5223
Match the right code to each word.

1 FROM _____   **3** FORM _____

2 ROOF _____   **4** MOOR _____

5 Using the same code, decode 5226 _____

Write the four-letter word hidden at the end of one word and the beginning of the next word. The order of the letters may not be changed.

Example: He liked fi<u>sh an</u>d chips.   <u>hand</u>

6 I was stung by a wasp in my garden.   _____

7 In the dusk the nightingales were singing.   _____

8 The team stays in cheap hotels to save money.   _____

9 The tide tugged at the tarred rope holding the anchor. _____

10 Ben and his friends ate three loaves of bread.   _____

Give a word that is similar in meaning to the word in capital letters and that rhymes with the second word.

Example: BATTLE   sight   <u>FIGHT</u>

11 DIVIDE   hair   _____

12 TALK   flat   _____

13 LABOUR   spoil   _____

14 ASCEND   rhyme   _____

15 SOIL   mirth   _____

Change the first word into the last word by changing one letter at a time, and making two new, different words in the middle.

Example: FLIP   <u>SLIP</u>   <u>SLIM</u>   SWIM

16 FLIT   _____   _____   PLAN

17 BUSY   _____   _____   BELT

18 PART   _____   _____   CORD

19 COIN   _____   _____   BARN

20 FLEX   _____   _____   BREW

Total [   ]

Rearrange the muddled letters in capitals to make a proper word.
The answer will complete the sentence sensibly.

Example: There are sixty SNODCES in a minute.   <u>seconds</u>

1   RAHSSK are fierce predators that live in the sea.   _____

2   Seven times ten equals VYSNTEE.   _____

3   GBRYU is a contact sport.   _____

4   There are many SHMLSEEO people on the London streets. _____

5   The ISOTRHC is the largest flightless bird.   _____

Underline two words, one from each group, that go together to form a new word.
The word in the first group always comes first.

Example: (light, <u>sun</u>, hot)   (sun, <u>shine</u>, summer)

6   (kind, hard, for)   (beds, nurses, wards)   9   (pick, ball, match) (stick, nick, miss)

7   (crack, break, mend) (slow, fast, full)   10   (water, free, tide) (sun, fall, wave)

8   (grand, after, before) (day, noon, hour)

Underline the two words that need to change places for each sentence to make sense.

Example: The <u>trees</u> were resting beneath the <u>elephants</u>.

11   Please close the quietly door.

12   Marion more one mark got than Jason.

13   In the snow the dark was falling softly.

14   Her shirt birthday present was the favourite.

15   He likes to play Saturdays on football.

BROTH   BROAD   BROOM   BROKE

If these words were written in alphabetical order which word would be:

16   first? _____   17   last? _____

Fill in the crossword so that all the words are included.

18–20 RARER   SUGAR
         SIDES   SAFER
         DRIER   FLING

Total

Complete the following sentences sensibly by selecting one word from each of the groups of words given in the brackets. Underline the words selected.

Example: The (man, <u>dog</u>, boy) chewed his (money, coffee, <u>bone</u>) in his (office, <u>kennel</u>, factory).

1 The footballer (picked, kicked, licked) the (ice cream, apple, ball) into the (back, stomach, heart) of the goal net.

2 The business (deal, class, man) took his (newspaper, sandwiches, desk) out of his briefcase and began to (read, eat, write) it.

3 (Why, Who, How) can I help you with your homework if (he, she, you) haven't brought your (books, cushions, hats) home?

4 At midday the grandfather (clock, man, chair) in our hallway (chimes, jumps, talks) (two, eight, twelve) times.

5 In order to (sleep, climb, write) neatly you will need to (eat, sharpen, break) your (pencil, knife, rubber).

Underline the one word in each group that cannot be made from the letters of the word in capital letters.

Example: BREAD   read   bard   <u>card</u>   bead   dear

6	ELASTIC	stile	scale	steal	stick	slice
7	GRAPEFRUIT	pager	treat	tiger	grate	purge
8	SPLENDOUR	round	proud	unless	loner	drops
9	STRAIGHT	shirt	right	thirst	stride	tights
10	PLEASANT	least	stale	plane	nasal	please

The code for the word BRIGHTER is 56174236. Encode each of these words using the same code.

11 GRIT _____   **12** TRIBE _____

Decode these codes using the same code as above.

13 4365 _____   **14** 431742 _____   **15** 21736 _____

Give the missing numbers in each sequence.

16 38   35   ___   29   ___   23   **17** 17   20   24   29   ___   ___

18 2   4   ___   16   32   ___

19 5   16   6   18   ___   ___   8   22

20 ___   17   44   ___   33   21   22   23

Total

Test time: 0 ——— 5 ——— 10 minutes

Fill in the crosswords so that all the words are included.

1–3

CHAIR RADAR

MOTOR CHASM

AWARD AWAIT

	▓		▓	
	▓		▓	
		A		

4–6

MEETS SHEDS

SOCKS OLIVE

CRIME STORM

	▓		▓	
O				
	▓		▓	

From the information supplied, underline the one statement below it that must be true.

7 My dustbin is black. My rubbish collection is on Thursdays.

    A All black dustbins are emptied on Thursdays.

    B My dustbin is emptied on Thursdays.

    C Thursday is a convenient day for rubbish collection.

    D My black dustbin is rubbish.

A B C D E F G H I J K L M N O P Q R S T U V W X Y Z

The word FLOWER is written in code as GMPXFS. Encode each of these words using the same code.

8 ROW _____   **9** LEAF _____

10 Decode TVOOZ using the same code.   _____

Move one letter from the first word to the second word to make two new words.

Example: BREAD COW   <u>BEAD</u>   <u>CROW</u>

11 SPEAR TEAK   _____   _____

12 MANGE HUE   _____   _____

13 FRAIL STAY   _____   _____

14 BROOM LED   _____   _____

15 TIRED TOUT   _____   _____

Write the four-letter word hidden at the end of one word and the beginning of the next word. The order of the letters may not be changed.

Example: He liked fi<u>sh and</u> chips.   <u>hand</u>

16 It was remarkable how fast army tanks appeared.   _____

17 The Australians batted until eleven o'clock.   _____

18 Watch out, there is a hair on that mouthful!   _____

19 I wish chocolate fountains would flow all the time.   _____

20 I catch the school bus to my village every day.   _____

Time for a break! Go to Puzzle Page 43 ▶

Total _____

Look at these words. Sort them into groups.

1–4

Ford	metre	Berlin	pineapple
Venice	Vauxhall	banana	millimetre

A	B	C	D
Cars	Measurements	Cities	Fruit
_____	_____	_____	_____
_____	_____	_____	_____

Add one letter to the word in capital letters to make a new word. The meaning of the new word is given in the clue.

Example: CANE   a tall, strong machine   <u>CRANE</u>

5	CEASE	a fold in material	_____
6	PLATE	the roof of your mouth	_____
7	READ	not looking forward to	_____
8	TAPER	to interfere with	_____

Underline the two words that are the odd ones out in each group of words.

Example: (house, office, <u>tractor</u>, bungalow, <u>chimney</u>)

9 (ring, circle, necklace, bracelet, box)   **11** (finger, nail, tack, screw, shoe)

10 (breakfast, lunch, cup, plate, dinner)   **12** (bite, tooth, chew, munch, lip)

Rearrange the letters in capitals to make a word that will match the description.

Example: BRUSH   it grows in the garden   <u>SHRUB</u>

13	STOAT	breakfast bread	_____
14	LEAST	not fresh	_____
15	REAPS	an extra one	_____
16	STAPLER	covers a wound	_____

Complete the following expressions by underlining the missing word.

Example: Frog is to tadpole as swan is to (duckling, baby, <u>cygnet</u>).

17 King is to crown as judge is to (wig, jury, bench).

18 Fish is to scales as bird is to (beak, wing, feathers).

19 Pig is to pork as cow is to (steak, beef, milk).

20 Hammer is to nail as spanner is to (screw, pin, nut).

Total

Underline one word in brackets that will go equally well with both pairs of words outside the brackets.

Example: world, planet   soil, ground   (night, space, <u>earth</u>, sphere)

1	examine, inspect	stop, limit	(test, check, restrain, study)
2	correctly, properly	brim, rise	(right, well, simply, spring)
3	imitate, mirror	think, consider	(reflect, demonstrate, ponder, return)
4	boundary, edge	confine, curb	(margin, pavement, limit, restrict)
5	affordable, inexpensive	second-rate, inferior	(mean, reasonable, low, cheap)

A B C D E F G H I J K L M N O P Q R S T U V W X Y Z

Fill in the missing letters.

6 ACF is to GIL as MOR is to _____   **9** ZW is to TQ as NK is to _____

7 ZX is to WU as TR is to _____   **10** AmD is to GnJ as MoP is to _____

8 ZA is to XC as VE is to _____

In her basket, Amy had beans, carrots, cucumber, mushrooms and tomatoes. Work out which section of the supermarket shelves she found her items on.

11–15   TOP

LEFT

cabbage	B	C	celery	potatoes
A	onions	D	E	broccoli

RIGHT

                    BOTTOM

The beans were somewhere above the mushrooms.
The cucumber was somewhere to the left of the tomatoes but not under the carrots.
The carrots, in turn, were directly above the mushrooms.

A = _____

B = _____

C = _____

D = _____

E = _____

The middle word in the first group has been made by taking two letters from the other two words. Complete the second group of three words in the same way, making a new word in the middle of the second group.

Example: PAIN INTO TOOK   ALSO <u>SOON</u> ONLY

16	SLAP	LACK	DOCK	PICK	_____	HEED
17	SORT	STOP	OPEN	FEEL	_____	OXEN
18	POOL	LOVE	SAVE	SEAL	_____	LIMB
19	MASH	SALE	TEAL	WAGE	_____	PERT
20	FLAG	GLAD	DRAB	SLIP	_____	GRUB

Total [   ]

Underline the two words, one from each group, which are the most opposite in meaning.

Example: (dawn, <u>early</u>, wake)   (<u>late</u>, stop, sunrise)

1	(off, under, up)	(on, through, by)
2	(steaming, warm, icy)	(cool, sleet, cold)
3	(for, again, by)	(up, through, against)
4	(leave, grant, give)	(pull, apply, take)
5	(point, sharp, apex)	(notice, blunt, hill)

A B C D E F G H I J K L M N O P Q R S T U V W X Y Z

Give the missing groups of letters in the following sequences.

6	AC	EG	IK	MO	QS	_____
7	ZP	YQ	XR	WS	VT	_____
8	CAD	DBE	ECF	FDG	GEH	_____
9	AZ	CX	EV	GT	IR	_____
10	feg	gfh	hgi	ihj	jik	_____

Find the letter that will end the first word and start the second word.

Example: FAS <u>T</u>   RACK

11	CLEA	____	EIGN		14	REL	____	ELL
12	SPAC	____	NJOY		15	TUNE	____	ESK
13	TRIC	____	ICKS					

Here are the number codes for four words.
9413 9471 7413 9331
Match the right code to each word.

16	LACK	_____
17	LAKE	_____
18	LEEK	_____
19	CAKE	_____

Decode this word using the same code as above.

| 20 | 1493 | _____ |

Total

Write the four-letter word hidden at the end of one word and the beginning of the next word. The order of the letters may not be changed.

Example: He liked fi<u>sh and</u> chips.   <u>hand</u>

1   We saw nothing but desert stretching before us.   _____

2   Mrs Smith knelt down to dust under the table.   _____

3   Neither the zebra nor the antelope heard the lion.   _____

4   The pies are in the oven.   _____

5   Some people think taking vitamins helps stop illnesses spreading. _____

From the information supplied, underline the one statement below it that must be true.

6   French is taught at our school. Our class has a French lesson on Friday.

   A All schools teach French.   **C** French is taught only on Friday.

   B We have a French lesson on Friday. **D** Our school is in France.

The code for the word CLOTHES is written as @!+?/*£. Decode these words using the same code as above.

7   @+£?   _____   **9**   @/**£*   _____

8   £@/++!   _____

Encode these words using the same code as above.

10 HOTEL   _____   **11** THOSE   _____

Choose two words, one from each set of brackets, to complete each sentence in the best way.

Example: Cat is to (<u>paw</u>, tail, furry) as horse is to (apple, neigh, <u>hoof</u>).

12 Pen is to (paper, write, biro) as brush is to (paint, blue, easel).

13 Wine is to bottle as (milk, petrol, meat) is to (mouth, garage, carton).

14 (Trousers, Top, Under) is to bottom as high is to (above, over, low).

15 Mind is to (think, read, care) as stomach is to (digest, fat, ache).

16 Go is to (get, come, stop) as green is to (amber, red, light).

If a=5, b=4, c=3, d=2 and e=1, find the value of:

17 $(a + b) - (c + d) =$ _____   **19** $(d^2 + c^2) - e =$ _____

18 $\dfrac{bc}{d} =$ _____   **20** $\dfrac{be}{d} + a =$ _____

Total _____

Give a word that is similar in meaning to the word in capital letters and that rhymes with the second word.

Example: BATTLE   sight   <u>FIGHT</u>

1	ENCLOSURE	dense	_____	**3**	LIQUID	course	_____
2	CONFUSE	cuddle	_____	**4**	SHARE	mice	_____

Find a word that can be put in front of each of the following words to make a new, compound word.

Example: day   set   burn   shine   <u>sun</u>

5	fall	mark	proof	colour	_____
6	fighter	work	side	arm	_____
7	man	drop	ball	flake	_____
8	forest	drop	coat	bow	_____

If these words are placed in alphabetical order, which comes fourth?

9	flatworm	flatbed	fledgling	flannel	flank	_____
10	stagnant	stagecoach	stagger	stadium	stainless	_____
11	harness	harmonic	harelip	harpoon	harrier	_____
12	larder	larva	larceny	lapwing	largesse	_____

Find the three-letter word that can be added to the letters in capitals to make a new word. The new word will complete the sentence sensibly. Write the three letter word.

Example: I watered the FERS in the garden.   <u>LOW</u>

13	Our car has new tyres on each WH.	_____
14	The headmaster said my H was too long and needed cutting.	_____
15	There are not enough chairs so he is STING.	_____
16	CRIES are a red fruit with a stone in the middle.	_____

A B C D E F G H I J K L M N O P Q R S T U V W X Y Z

Give the next group of letters in each sequence.

17	AX	DU	GR	JO	ML	____
18	WV	YX	AZ	CB	ED	____
19	GQ	HQ	IR	JR	KS	____
20	BW	BV	CU	CT	DS	____

Total [   ]

Test time: 0 |||||| 5 ||||| 10 minutes

Underline the pair of words most opposite in meaning.

Example: halt, stop   broad, wide   <u>cheap, expensive</u>

1	win, lose	win, success	failure, disappointment
2	hot, cool	warm, cool	cold, warm
3	clear, lucid	cloudy, rainy	clear, cloudy
4	stand, deliver	collect, deliver	send, deliver

Rearrange the muddled letters in capitals to make a proper word.
The answer will complete the sentence sensibly.

Example: There are sixty SNODCES in a minute.   <u>SECONDS</u>

5   In October we have a EVAHSRT festival service at school.   _____

6   I will go to secondary school when I am VNLEEE.   _____

7   The BMANLCUAE is coming to take the sick man to hospital.   _____

8   Tania's father is a car CANHMIEC at the garage.   _____

Underline one of the words in brackets that goes best with the words given outside the brackets.

Example: rapid, fast   (slow, rate, run, <u>haste</u>)

9   dash, shoot (arrow, dart, rifle, jog)   **11**   expel, emit   (school, bully, reject, eject)

10   light, just   (true, pale, fair, time)   **12**   portly, heavy (weight, harbour, stout, stone)

Move one letter from the first word to the second word to make two new words.

Example: BREAD COW <u>BEAD</u>   <u>CROW</u>

13   CRANE   BED   _____   _____   **15**   SUET   URN   _____   _____

14   PLIGHT   CAR   _____   _____   **16**   FLOOD   HIT   _____   _____

Underline the two words that are made from the same letters.

Example: <u>seat</u>   state   rates   trait   <u>eats</u>

17	shears	sheep	shapes	phases	shorts
18	strong	grunts	grants	strain	strung
19	staple	please	palest	apples	scrape
20	blast	stole	stale	label	least

Total

Look at these groups of words.

A	B	C	D	E
pencil	oak	seaside	table	trout
ruler	elm	sandcastle	cupboard	carp

Choose the correct group for each of these words below. Write in the group letter.

1–5   beech ____   rubber ____   perch ____   pike ____   beach ____

       bed ____   pen ____   pine ____   chair ____   seaweed ____

Take away one letter from the word in capital letters to make a new word.
The meaning of the new word is given in the clue.

Example: SPEED   you plant it   <u>SEED</u>

6	FRAME	well known	_____
7	CHEAT	to make hotter	_____
8	PLANT	organise	_____
9	CRATER	supply	_____
10	LADDER	snake	_____

Choose the word from the group in brackets that is opposite to the word in capitals.

Example: HEALTHY   (strong, energetic, hospital, <u>ill</u>)

11	THIN	(thick, healthy, full, emaciated)
12	EASY	(simple, facile, difficult, descriptive)
13	FULL	(avoid, replete, refill, empty)
14	FLAT	(level, uneven, square, apartment)
15	QUIET	(noisy, quite, crowded, whispering)

Underline the pair of words most similar in meaning.

Example: hot, cold   <u>dish, bowl</u>   tea, coffee

16	high, low	climb, ascend	lift, descend
17	polite, impolite	before, now	concur, agree
18	healthy, well	well, lake	health, happiness
19	dart, dodge	dodge, budge	arrow, dart
20	pillow, bed	carpet, rug	bucket, spade

Total

Choose two words, one from each set of brackets, to complete each sentence in the best way.

Example: Cat is to (<u>paw</u>, tail, furry) as horse is to (apple, neigh, <u>hoof</u>).

1   Book is to (library, author, paper) as money is to (cash, bank, exchange).

2   Saturday is to (weekend, supermarket, holiday) as Monday is to (washing, weekday, school).

3   Tooth is to (bite, filling, mouth) as beak is to (nest, worms, peck).

4   Apple is to (wine, juice, pip) as peach is to (apricot, stone, tree).

5   Oar is to (mine, ship, boat) as pedal is to (bicycle, horse, pushers).

Change the first word into the last word by changing one letter at a time, and making two new, different words in the middle.

Example: FLIP   <u>SLIP</u>   <u>SLIM</u>   SWIM

6	GATE	_____	_____	SOME	**9**	BASK	_____	_____	BOTH
7	PLAN	_____	_____	PREY	**10**	WORK	_____	_____	FONT
8	SIZE	_____	_____	MUTE					

Underline two words, one from each group, that go together to form a new word. The word in the first group always comes first.

Example: (light, <u>sun</u>, hot)   (sun, <u>shine,</u> summer)

11   (old, space, fishing) (age, ship, boat)   **14**   (pigs, bulls, birds)   (eye, ear, nose)

12   (road, lane, street)   (works, stop, gear)   **15**   (bread, stick, head) (short, long, wide)

13   (darling, honey, hare) (brush, hive, comb)

From the information supplied, answer the questions.

There were 23 different types of cheese on a cheese counter at the farm shop.
There were four different types of soft goats' cheese, two of these were Welsh, the rest English.
There were seven other types of soft cheese; five cows' cheeses and two cheeses made from milk taken from sheep. All these were English.
There were 12 hard cows' cheeses, three from Wales and two from Ireland.

16   How many soft cheeses were there?   _____

17   Are the sheep's cheeses soft or hard?   _____

18   How many English hard cheeses were there?   _____

19   How many Welsh cheeses were there altogether?   _____

20   How many English cheeses were there altogether?   _____

Time for a break! Go to Puzzle Page 44

Total _____

Underline the two words, one from each group, which are closest in meaning.

Example: (fat, short, <u>slim</u>)   (strong, heavy, <u>thin</u>)

1 (headlong, headstrong, headline) (stubborn, lengthy, mark)

2 (clothes, line, border) (flower, straight, edge)

3 (edgy, calm, sensible) (tender, tense, hectic)

4 (pirate, mutiny, crew) (revolt, repulse, revive)

5 (power, tower, mower) (length, width, strength)

Complete the following sentences sensibly by selecting one word from each of the groups of words given in the brackets. Underline the words selected.

Example: The (man, <u>dog</u>, boy) chewed his (money, coffee, <u>bone</u>) in his (office, <u>kennel</u>, factory).

6 My aunt listens to (music, tortoises, trees) on the (bathroom, radio, dustbin).

7 I (spoke, saw, ran) to Jo on the (television, park, telephone).

8 "Kindly (eat, leave, climb) those (tomatoes, stairs, books) alone!" shouted the (desk, teacher, goldfish).

9 A (hippo, giraffe, mouse) lives mostly in African (rivers, houses, airports) and has a big (ear, mouth, neck).

10 Before Adam (combs, counts, brushes) his teeth in the (classroom, morning, jungle) he likes to wash his face with his (flannel, hairbrush, dog).

A B C D E F G H I J K L M N O P Q R S T U V W X Y Z

Give the missing groups of letters or numbers in each sequence.

11 CL ___ EN FO GP HQ

12 GT HS IR JQ KP ___

13 FY FW GU GS ___ HO

14 506 ___ 524 533 542 551

15 17 ___ 20 20 23 30

16 24 25 23 24 21 ___

Find a word that can be put in front of each of the following words to make a new, compound word.

Example: day   set   burn   shine   <u>sun</u>

17 owner   fill   lady   mark   _____

18 life   cat   fowl   fire   _____

19 ness   lighter   light   land   _____

20 swept   surfing   screen   pipe   _____

Total

Find the letter that will end the first word and start the second word.

Example: FAS <u>T</u> RACK

1 LAS __ OAK   **3** RU __ EWT   **5** KIT __ LSE

2 GRU __ OOK   **4** NI __ OLE

Fill in the crosswords so that all the words are included.

6–8

EARLY   NOSEY

EAGER   PREEN

PIECE   EDGES

9–11

STEAL   FLASH

HOTEL   FIRES

ANGLE   RIGHT

Underline the two words that need to change places for each sentence to make sense.

Example: The <u>trees</u> were resting beneath the <u>elephants</u>.

12 Put did you where the car keys?

13 Sam promised to morning up early in the get.

14 The batsman hit the pavilion over the ball.

15 He found a table he really liked on a book.

Write the four-letter word hidden at the end of one word and the beginning of the next word. The order of the letters may not be changed.

Example: He liked fi<u>sh and</u> chips.   <u>hand</u>

16 My uncle says you must take the rough with the smooth. _____

17 The teacher was very angry with all the class. _____

18 Mrs Blewitt says they are stored in her greenhouse. _____

19 Mandy has gone to collect all the hockey balls. _____

20 A young swallow has migrated with the rest of the birds. _____

Total

If the months were put in alphabetical order, which would be:

1 the second last month? _____

2 the third month? _____

3 the month after June? _____

A B C D E F G H I J K L M N O P Q R S T U V W X Y Z

The word BOTTLE is written in code as ANSSKD. Encode each of these words using the same code.

4 PENCIL _____

5 CRAYON _____

Decode these words using the same code as above.

6 RONNMR _____

7 OKZSDR _____

Give the missing numbers in each sequence.

8   ___ ___ 36 41 46 51

9   5 9 6 10 7 ___ ___

10 4 8 ___ 32 ___ 128

11 16 9 18 7 ___ ___ 22 3

Underline the two words from the group which are most similar in type or meaning.

Example: <u>dear</u> pleasant poor extravagant <u>expensive</u>

12 touch feel smoke laugh ring

13 hammer nail finger tack varnish

14 coal gem oar majesty paddle

15 neighbour teacher friend niece instructor

Underline the two words, one from each group, that go together to form a new word. The word in the first group always comes first.

Example: (light, <u>sun</u>, hot) (sun, <u>shine</u>, summer)

16 (sea, green, black) (berry, current, piece)

17 (turn, right, arm) (gate, stop, chair)

18 (ground, round, water) (under, about, place)

19 (pillow, briefs, picnic) (place, case, sheet)

20 (vegetable, grass, hedge) (wood, green, row)

Total

Underline one word in brackets that will go equally well with both pairs of words outside the brackets.

Example: world, planet   soil, ground   (night, space, <u>earth</u>, sphere)

1   just, equal   blonde, light   (fair, plus, yellow, appropriate)

2   correct, precise   fix, mend   (exact, wrong, right, sum)

3   undecorated, simple   clear, direct   (easy, ugly, flat, plain)

4   wealthy, affluent   unhealthy, creamy   (satisfactory, well, rich, correctly)

If a=2, b=5, c=4, d=3 and e=10, find the value of:

5 $d + a + c =$ _____   **6** $\dfrac{e}{a} + b =$ _____   **7** $\dfrac{de}{b} =$ _____   **8** $(e - d) + (b - c) =$ _____

Write the four-letter word hidden at the end of one word and the beginning of the next word. The order of the letters may not be changed.

Example: He liked fi<u>sh and</u> chips.   <u>hand</u>

9   If you push other people out of the way, you will be punished.   _____

10   Ruby's new bike had a black frame and a white saddle.   _____

11   It takes forty minutes to cook my lasagne.   _____

12   She counted the hours until the bell rang.   _____

Find the three-letter word that can be added to the letters in capitals to make a new word. The new word will complete the sentence sensibly. Write the three-letter word.

Example: I watered the FERS in the garden.   <u>LOW</u>

13   The JNEY to Scotland took a long time.   _____

14   The old man had a long grey BD.   _____

15   Don't burn yourself on the SM from the kettle.   _____

16   The BEA finalist congratulated the winner.   _____

Underline the one word in each group that cannot be made from the letters of the word in capital letters.

Example: BREAD	read	bard	<u>card</u>	bead	dear
17 PILLOWCASE	swallow	lapse	scalp	callow	scale
18 CHARACTER	crater	charter	earth	teacher	reach
19 CHROMOSOME	choose	morose	chrome	rooms	cross
20 TRANSITION	artist	nations	noise	strait	station

Total

Find the two letters that will end the first word and start the second word.

Example: FRU <u>IT</u> EM

1	PET	___	TER	**3**	KNI	___	ARLESS
2	HAND	___	DGE	**4**	MOU	___	ORN

Rearrange the letters in capitals to make another word. The answer will match the description.

Example: BRUSH   it grows in the garden   <u>SHRUB</u>

5	CHEAP	a juicy fruit	_____
6	PLATE	part of a flower	_____
7	SCALP	pin part of a brooch	_____
8	STRUT	belief	_____

Look at these words. Sort them into groups.

9–12   Brian   bus   for   train   under   squash   Susan   beer

A	B	C	D
Names	Transport	Drinks	Prepositions
_____	_____	_____	_____
_____	_____	_____	_____

Underline the word in brackets closest in meaning to the word in capitals.

Example: HEALTHY (<u>strong</u>, energetic, hospital, ill)

13	BLUE	(bruise, sky, downfall, azure)	**15**	CRY	(weep, call, say, tearful)
14	CALM	(rough, kind, tranquil, stormy)	**16**	STUBBLE	(field, straw, bristle, fall)

From the information supplied, complete the statements.

I was 4 when my brother was born. My father was 8 times older than I was then.

17   When my father is 40 my brother will be _____ years old.

18   When I am 16, my brother will be _____ years old.

From the information supplied, answer the questions.

Z is a number. Double it and take away 2. Divide by 3 and the answer is 6.

19   What is Z ?   _____

20   What would Z be if you take away 8 instead of 2?   _____

Total

Test time: 0 | | | | | 5 | | | | | 10 minutes

Complete the following sentences sensibly by selecting one word from each of the groups of words given in brackets. Underline the words selected.

Example: The (man, <u>dog</u>, boy) chewed his (money, coffee, <u>bone</u>) in his (office, <u>kennel</u>, factory).

1   The (tennis, football, golf) player lifted his (club, racquet, shirt) and hit the ball into the (yard, goal, court).

2   The (banana, goldfish, man) (swam, climbed, lay) around the bowl amongst the (pondweed, kitchen, salad).

3   The weather forecaster said the (rain, weather, cloud) would be (weather, rainy, map) this afternoon with snow on high (ground, tea, cloud).

From the information supplied, answer the questions.

A family went to the swimming baths and put their clothes in different lockers.
Mum, Sarah and Tom put their clothes in lockers next door to each other.
Pete put his in the locker opposite Tom's. Dad and Sarah used even numbered lockers.
The empty lockers are shaded. Who used which locker?

4   Locker 3   _____

5   Locker 4   _____

6   Locker 5   _____

7   Locker 12 _____

8   Locker 14 _____

1	2	3	4	5	6	7
8	9	10	11	12	13	14

Give a word that is similar in meaning to the word in capital letters and that rhymes with the second word.

Example: BATTLE sight   <u>FIGHT</u>

9   MISERY   beef   _____

10   PRETTY   suit   _____

11   QUIVER   brake   _____

12   CONCEIT   wide   _____

13   FASHION   friend   _____

14   POUR   thrush   _____

Here are the number codes for four words.
9480   0643   9064   9884
Match the right code to the right word.

15   SWAN _____   16   SOON _____   17   WANT_____   18   SNOW _____

Decode these words using the same code as above.

19   3804 _____   20   6439 _____

Total

The middle word in the first group has been made by taking two letters from the other two words.
Complete the second group of three words in the same way, making a new word in the middle of the second group.

Example: PAIN INTO TOOK   ALSO <u>SOON</u> ONLY

1	SIZE	ZEST	STUN	TYPE	_____	ARCH
2	TRIP	PILL	TELL	FATS	_____	DROP
3	SEER	REED	ENDS	WICK	_____	NAGS
4	EBBS	SEEN	NEWT	EMIT	_____	LAMB
5	FEUD	DUET	TRAM	CUPS	_____	ROUT

Underline the two words, one from each group, which are the most opposite in meaning.

Example: (dawn, <u>early</u>, wake)   (<u>late</u>, stop, sunrise)

6 (complete, compete, compel) (entire, start, win)

7 (hide, expose, cruise) (depose, conceal, decrease)

8 (stately, friendly, distant) (approachable, anger, dislike)

9 (dead, genuine, alive) (real, blunt, fake)

10 (praise, practise, prance) (criticise, compliment, commend)

From the information supplied, underline the one statement below it that must be true.

11 Sheena was given a pot plant. It was not watered so it died.

A The plant was a birthday present.   **C** Sheena liked plants.

B Sheena was too busy to water the plant.   **D** The plant needed water to stay alive.

If a=10, b=4, c=3 and d=5, find the value of the following.

12 $\dfrac{ab}{d} =$ ___   **13** $(b+c) - (a - d) =$ ___   **14** $\dfrac{bd}{a} + c =$ ___   **15** $(b - c) + ac =$ ___

Write the letters in the following words in alphabetical order.

16 PLASTIC _____   **18** NURSEMAID _____

17 SCAMPER _____   **19** KEYBOARD _____

From the information supplied answer the question.

I appear twice in INNUMERABLE, once in SINCE and not at all in NATIONAL.

20 Which letter is being described? ____

Total

Test time: 0 | | | | | 5 | | | | | 10 minutes

Find the one letter that will end the first word and start the second word of each pair of words. The same letter must be used for both pairs of words.

Example: FAS <u>T</u> RACK   DEN <u>T</u> WIN

1   STAF ___ OXES   CLIF ___ ADES   **3**   TRAI ___ IGHT   TOXI ___ AILS

2   STA ___ LUE   FRO ___ REET   **4**   JA ___ AIL   STRA ___ HEN

Choose two words, one from each set of brackets, to complete each sentence in the best way.

Example: Cat is to (<u>paw</u>, tail, furry) as horse is to (apple, neigh, <u>hoof</u>).

5   Dusk is to (sunset, evening, dark) as dawn is to (beginning, hours, morning).

6   Blue is to (sky, black, navy) as red is to (orange, blood, ruby).

7   Fact is to (truth, guess, idea) as opinion is to (proof, evidence, belief).

8   Fall is to (drop, water, autumn) as descend is to (lower, raise, winter).

Change the first word into the last word by changing one letter at a time, and making two new, different words in the middle.

Example: FLIP <u>SLIP</u>   <u>SLIM</u>   SWIM

9   WALK   _____ _____   PILL   **11**   LIFT   _____ _____   LAME

10 TRAY   _____ _____   DRIP   **12**   SHOE   _____ _____   BOOT

Underline two words, one from each group, that go together to form a new word. The word in the first group always comes first.

Example: (light, <u>sun</u>, hot)   (sun, <u>shine</u>, summer)

13   (home, guest, hotel)   (going, work, bill)

14   (yolk, egg, soup)   (plate, pudding, shell)

15   (back, drake, lever)   (let, wards, for)

16   (low, high, grand)   (sit, stand, seat)

Rearrange the muddled letters in capitals to make a proper word. The answer will complete the sequence sensibly.

Example: There are 60 SNODCES in a minute.   <u>SECONDS</u>

17   CRAFIA is a hot and varied continent.   _____

18   Not all snakes are OIOUNPSSO.   _____

19   NERHTITE is a prime number.   _____

20   Queen TBZLEIAEH I was Henry VIII's daughter.   _____

(33)

Total

Underline the two words that are made from the same letters.

Example: <u>seat</u>   state   rates   trait   <u>eats</u>

1	easel	least	slats	lease	steel	**3**	rasps	spore	spare	prose	spoon
2	worst	wrath	throw	worth	threw	**4**	check	cheap	teach	threat	cheat

A B C D E F G H I J K L M N O P Q R S T U V W X Y Z

Fill in the missing letters, symbols or numbers.

5 A/C is to E\G as Q/S is to _____

7 f14H is to j20L as r31T is to _____

6 G25 is to H30 as O65 is to _____

8 HgF is to EdC as BaZ is to _____

Find a word that can be put in front of each of the following words to make a new, compound word.

Example: day   set   burn   shine   <u>sun</u>

9	time	clothes	room	spread	_____
10	board	list	mail	bird	_____
11	time	long	boat	guard	_____
12	thing	one	where	how	_____

Complete the following sentences sensibly by selecting one word from each of the groups of words given in the brackets. Underline the words selected.

Example: The (man, <u>dog</u>, boy) chewed his (money, coffee, <u>bone</u>) in his (office, <u>kennel</u>, factory).

13 It was raining so (soft, slowly, hard) that the river burst its (banks, balloons, beds) and flooded the (crowd, road, river).

14 Before going to (school, church, bed) at night, Tracey puts on her (pyjamas, anorak, skis) and brushes her (shoes, carpets, hair).

15 Sometimes on Fridays, we have fish and (fingers, chips, rods) for (French, lunch, pudding) at (school, breakfast, Christmas).

16 We arrived late at the (cinema, ferry, shop) so had to (eat, rest, hurry) to see the beginning of the (book, film, concert).

If i=10, j=12, k=4, l=5, m=3 and n=2, find the value of the following. Write your answers as letters.

17 $\dfrac{jl}{i} + k =$ _____

19 $k^2 - n^2 =$ _____

18 $(i + m + n) - j =$ _____

20 $\dfrac{j}{m} - \dfrac{i}{l} =$ _____

Total

TEST 34: **Mixed**

A B C D E F G H I J K L M N O P Q R S T U V W X Y Z

Give the missing groups of letters or numbers in each sequence.

1	GHI	KLM	____	STU	____	ABC	
2	66	17	55	27	44	____	____	47
3	a6	C12	e18	____	i30	K36	m42	____
4	3	6	____	____	21	28	36	45

Underline one word in brackets that will go equally well with both pairs of words outside the brackets.

Example: world, planet   <u>soil</u>, ground   (night, space, <u>earth</u>, sphere)

5	muscular, powerful	solid, stable	(frozen, strong, long-lasting, consistent)
6	inner, inside	centre, core	(interior, inland, exterior, indoors)
7	instructor, tutor	teach, drill	(scout, bus, coach, student)
8	hobby, activity	attention, curiosity	(interview, interfere, interest, intercept)

Underline the one word in each group that cannot be made from the letters of the word in capital letters.

Example: BREAD   read   bard   <u>card</u>   bead   dear

9	NESTLING	sting	sling	tingle	gentle	listen
10	PINEAPPLE	apple	pliant	plain	plane	nipple
11	SCRATCHING	chain	racing	string	crash	search
12	MAINSTREAM	strain	mares	master	trains	matter

Find the three-letter word that can be added to the letters in capitals to make a new word. The new word will complete the sentence sensibly. Write the three-letter word.

Example: I watered the FERS in the garden.   <u>LOW</u>

13	The door HLE has broken.	_____
14	We have lots of GS on our farm.	_____
15	Ben spilt the bottle of SPOO in the bathroom.	_____
16	Some metals are MAGIC.	_____

Which one letter can be added to the front of all of the words to make new words?

Example: _air   _ear   _lute   <u>f</u>

17	_ash	_art	_hart	____	**19**	_arrow	_early	_either	____
18	_arched	_ill	_inch	____	**20**	_pen	_pal	_wing	____

Total

Rearrange the letters in capitals to make a word that matches the description.

Example: BRUSH   it grows in the garden   <u>SHRUB</u>

1   PLEASE   opposite of awake   _____

2   STRIPE   holy man   _____

3   TILLERS   a support for plants   _____

4   PASSED   tools used for digging   _____

Add one letter to the word in capital letters to make a new word. The meaning of the new word is given in the clue.

Example: CANE   a tall, strong machine   <u>CRANE</u>

5   STEAM   a small river   _____

6   HEARS   a cutting tool   _____

7   SALLOW   not deep   _____

8   BELOW   to shout   _____

Underline the two words that are the odd ones out in each group of words.

Example: (house, office, <u>tractor</u>, bungalow, <u>chimney</u>)

9   (scare, crow, fright, shock, clock)

10   (pencil, rubber, ruler, pen, biro)

11   (history, geography, biology, classroom, teacher)

12   (cube, triangle, square, pyramid, rectangle)

Complete the following expressions by underlining the missing word.

Example: Frog is to tadpole as swan is to (duckling, baby, <u>cygnet</u>).

13   Chair is to four as stool is to (kitchen, three, legs).

14   Fish is to fin as cow is to (calf, milk, hoof).

15   Box is to lid as house is to (roof, chimney, upstairs).

16   Gravel is to drive as sand is to (castle, beach, Blackpool).

Underline any words below that contain only the first six letters of the alphabet.

17	coffee	beach	efface	dabble	dance
18	pebble	back	clubs	basin	added
19	fiction	freckle	fatigue	fudge	faced
20	abacus	dead	dread	cradle	adding

Total

The code for the word CHRISTMAS is *!/%?\£:?. Encode each of these words using the same code.

1 SHIRT _____

2 MARCH _____

Decode these words using the same code as above.

3 ?\/%*\ _____

4 :??%?\ _____

The code for the word DABBLE is 4 1 2 2 12 5. Encode each of these words using the same code.

5 CABLE _____

6 FACED _____

Fill in the crosswords so that all the words are included.

7–9

			U		

10–12

				P	

CLAIMS STRONG ARMOUR

ENDING ALMOND CRADLE

DEEPER LARGER BOUNDS

SUDDEN UDDERS BUSTLE

Write the four-letter word hidden at the end of one word and the beginning of the next word. The order of the letters may not be changed.

Example: He liked fi<u>sh an</u>d chips. <u>hand</u>

13 Dad asked me if I knew why our radio was broken. _____

14 My aunt took her children to the theme park. _____

15 Deborah's temper got the better of her in class. _____

16 The police raided one address in Birmingham. _____

From the following information, answer the questions.

The village of Ashley is due north of Calne and due east of the village of Bourne which, in turn, is due north of Dalton. The four villages make the corners of a square.

17 Which village is west of Ashley? _____

18 Which village is south of Bourne? _____

19 Which direction is Calne from Ashley? _____

20 Which direction is Calne from Bourne? _____

Total _____

Change the first word into the last word by changing one letter at a time, and making two new, different words in the middle.

Example: FLIP   <u>SLIP</u>   <u>SLIM</u>   SWIM

1   PLAN   _____ _____   STAY

2   TYPE   _____ _____   SORE

3   CLIP   _____ _____   CROW

4   SOUL   _____ _____   FOOT

Which one letter can be added to the front of all of the words to make new words?

Example: _air   _are   _ear   _lop   _lute   <u>f</u>

5   _rain   _lend   _rake   _east   _and   ____

6   _end   _out   _ever   _earn   _awful   ____

7   _scent   _maze   _wake   _shore   _jar   ____

8   _lad   _orge   _amble   _listen   _range   ____

A B C D E F G H I J K L M N O P Q R S T U V W X Y Z

Fill in the missing symbols, letters or numbers, or underline the words.

9   AZ is to FU as HS is to _____

10   ZBE is to GIL as NPS is to _____

11   Butterfly is to nectar as (pillowcase, caterpillar, lion) is to (bed, leaf, pillow).

12   Slow is to tortoise as (flat, brush, fast) is to (hedgehog, pancake, hare).

13   T17 is to Q20 as L25 is to _____

14   ?!£% is to %£!? as @$/; is to _____

15   Bow is to arrow as (dart, gun, target) is to (bullet, gun, target).

16   Speed is to speedometer as (time, race, supersonic) is to (clock, car, jet).

Underline the two words that need to change places for each sentence to make sense.

Example: The <u>trees</u> were resting beneath the <u>elephants</u>.

17   Guinea-pigs feeds her Sally every day before breakfast.

18   For lunch today we had roast salad followed by fruit chicken.

19   I am maths my finding homework hard.

20   My favourite starts programme television at 8.00pm.

Total

Complete the third pair in the same way as the other pairs.

Example: bind, hind   bare, hare   but, <u>hut</u>

1	glad, lad	about, bout	climb, _____
2	pray, prayer	train, trainer	toast, _____
3	pat, pout	flat, flout	rat, _____
4	sludge, slug	fudge, fug	budge, _____
5	frame, blame	fright, blight	frown, _____

Underline one of the words in brackets to go with the word beside it, in the same way as the first two words go together.

Example: good, better   bad, (naughty, worst, <u>worse</u>, nasty)

6	short, tall	wide, (empty, fat, broad, narrow)
7	through, around	under, (beneath, over, next, by)
8	chatter, babble	talk, (quiet, silent, speak, noise)
9	delicate, flimsy	light, (illuminate, heavy, darken, substantial)
10	laces, tie	button, (chocolate, fasten, trousers, nose)

A B C D E F G H I J K L M N O P Q R S T U V W X Y Z
Give the missing groups of letters or numbers in each sequence.

11	45	16	____	20	35	____	30	28
12	4	8	7	_____	_____	14	13	17
13	p4	q6	r9	s13	____	u24	____	w39
14	ACZ	BDY	CEX	DFW	EGV	FHU	____	____
15	ADb	____	ILj	MPn	QTr	UXv	YBz	____	GjH

The middle word in the first group has been made by taking two letters from the other two words. Complete the second group of three words in the same way, making a new word in the middle of the second group.

Example: PAIN INTO   TOOK   ALSO <u>SOON</u>   ONLY

16	SPOT	TOAD	RAID	BOOM	_____	SALT
17	CATS	STAB	BILE	BIRD	_____	PINK
18	TRIP	PINT	PANT	FEAR	_____	GRID
19	SLOW	WOOL	POSH	SLAT	_____	KILL
20	TEAM	MEAT	MILE	LEAF	_____	DICE

Total

From the information supplied, answer the questions.

Naomi, Fern, Husna and Debra are friends at secondary school.
Fern, Naomi and Husna learn Spanish.   Husna, Fern and Debra study French.
Naomi, Husna and Debra study Art   Debra, Fern and Naomi do Chemistry.
Husna learns Greek.   Fern and Debra do Geography.
Debra and Naomi do Textiles.   Fern and Husna do Music.

1   Who does French but does not do Art?   _____

2   Who does Chemistry but not Geography?   _____

3   Who does Art and Spanish but not Geography or Textiles? _____

4   Who does not study Music, Greek or Spanish?   _____

5   Who does the least subjects?   _____

A B C D E F G H I J K L M N O P Q R S T U V W X Y Z
The code for the word CANDLE is ECPFNG. Using the same code:

Encode these words.   Decode these words.

6   LIGHT   _____   **8**   NWEMA _____

7   DARKNESS _____   **9**   ETCBA _____

Complete the following expressions by underlining the missing word.

Example: Frog is to tadpole as swan is to (duckling, baby, <u>cygnet</u>).

10   Solid is to rigid as strong is to (liquid, weak, sturdy).

11   Thrash is to defeat as crush is to (conquer, draw, defy).

12   Accurate is to inaccurate as true is to (real, genuine, false).

13   Hard is to firm as coarse is to (dinner, harsh, smooth).

14   Modest is to proud as humble is to (meek, arrogant, lowly).

Write the following letters or words in alphabetical order.

15   DRAUGHT _____   **16**   COMPUTER _____

17   DREAM   DRAWN   DRAWL   _____

18   HEARTH   HEATER   HEARTY   _____

19   In alphabetical order, which day of the week comes after Monday? _____

From the information supplied, answer the question.

I appear twice in INCORRUPTIBLE, once in RIDDLE and not at all in PENCIL.

20   Which letter is being described? ____

Total

A B C D E F G H I J K L M N O P Q R S T U V W X Y Z

Give the missing groups of letters or numbers in each sequence.

1	6	15	___	___	18	9	24	6
2	___	___	XCD	WDE	VEF	UFG	TGH	SHI
3	60h	50g	41f	33e	26d	20c	___	___
4	BCa	FGe	JKi	NÓm	___	VWu	___	DEc

Change the first word into the last word by changing one letter at a time, and making two new, different words in the middle.

Example: FLIP   <u>SLIP</u>   <u>SLIM</u>   SWIM

5	WOOD	_____	_____	WARE	**9**	PYRE	_____	_____	SURF
6	NOSE	_____	_____	RICE	**10**	BEST	_____	_____	GOAT
7	LAZY	_____	_____	TAME	**11**	PLEA	_____	_____	FLOW
8	MICE	_____	_____	RISK	**12**	COME	_____	_____	HOST

Which one letter can be added to the front of all of the words to make new words?

Example: air   _are   _ear   _lop   _lute   <u>f</u>

13	_heel	_hat	_all	_hale	_eighty	___
14	_eight	_erring	_eel	_edge	_earth	___
15	_otter	_ark	_light	_honey	_rattle	___
16	_lope	_at	_bony	_state	_vent	___

Eight people went to the theatre. The unshaded seats are the ones they have tickets for. Using the information below, work out where each person sat.

Judy sat next to her sister.

Clement sat next to Pravin.

Gretel sat right at the side of the theatre.

Harold sat nearer Kang than anyone else.

Kang sat to the left of Harold.

Sandra sat directly three rows behind Pravin.

Penelope sat diagonally in front of Sandra.

FRONT

STAGE

1C 1D

2F 2G   2J

LEFT   3E   RIGHT

4D 4E

BACK

17–20   1C = _____   1D = _____

2F = _____   2G = _____   2J = _____

3E = _____   4D = _____   4E = _____

Time for a break! Go to Puzzle Page 46 ▶

Total

Puzzle ①

Take the words and place them in the grid so that each word reads horizontally and vertically.

Example:

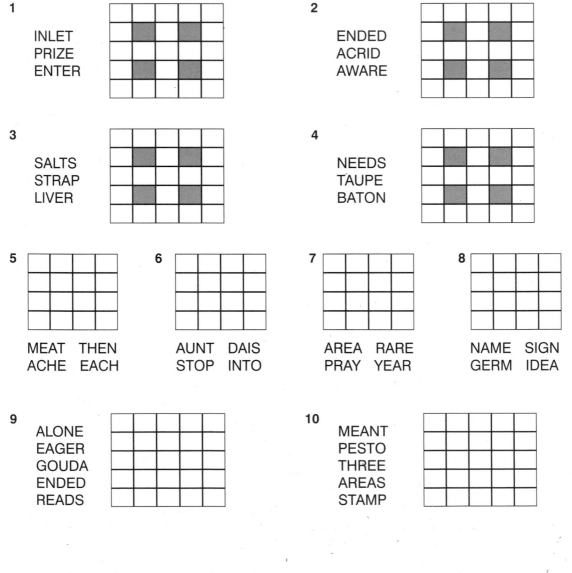

EVERY
BREAD
DOYEN

B	R	E	A	D
R		V		O
E	V	E	R	Y
A		R		E
D	O	Y	E	N

1

INLET
PRIZE
ENTER

2

ENDED
ACRID
AWARE

3

SALTS
STRAP
LIVER

4

NEEDS
TAUPE
BATON

5

MEAT   THEN
ACHE   EACH

6

AUNT   DAIS
STOP   INTO

7

AREA   RARE
PRAY   YEAR

8

NAME   SIGN
GERM   IDEA

9

ALONE
EAGER
GOUDA
ENDED
READS

10

MEANT
PESTO
THREE
AREAS
STAMP

Puzzle ❷

Help Freddy to jump from one lily-pad to the next by changing one letter at a time.
Watch out! The clues have been mixed up!

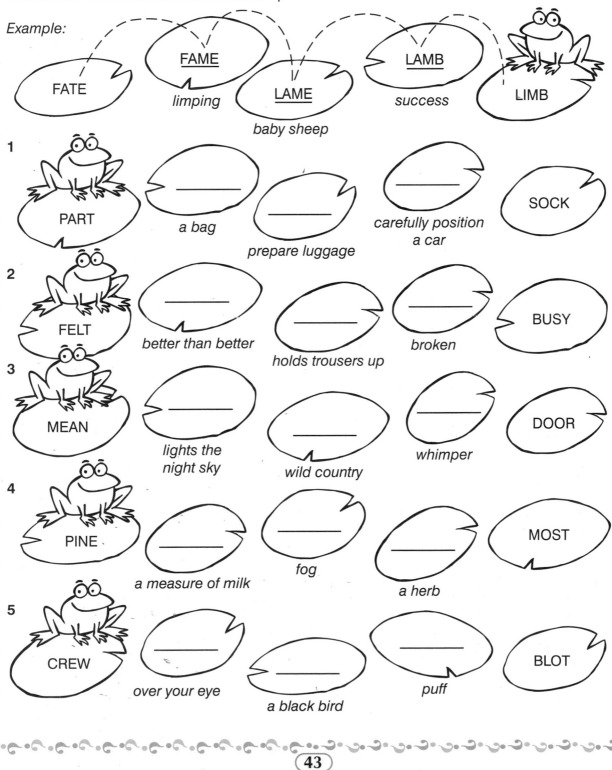

Example:

FATE → FAME → LAME → LAMB → LIMB

limping

baby sheep

success

1 PART → _____ → _____ → _____ → SOCK

a bag

prepare luggage

carefully position a car

2 FELT → _____ → _____ → _____ → BUSY

better than better

holds trousers up

broken

3 MEAN → _____ → _____ → _____ → DOOR

lights the night sky

wild country

whimper

4 PINE → _____ → _____ → _____ → MOST

a measure of milk

fog

a herb

5 CREW → _____ → _____ → _____ → BLOT

over your eye

a black bird

puff

Puzzle ③

Lucy, Clare, James and Jamila were all taken to Blackpool for a day trip over the summer holidays. Each of them was taken by an older relative. In the afternoon, before they went home, they were allowed one last treat.

From the information below, and using the grid to help you, work out which relative was with each child and what treat each of them chose. Fill in the table at the bottom of the page when you have worked it all out.

	mum	grandpa	aunt	sister	funfair	donkey ride	ice cream	beach games
Lucy								
Clare								
James		X						
Jamila								
funfair				
donkey ride				
ice cream				
beach games				

Grandpa sat in a deck-chair while his granddaughter had a donkey ride.
Jamila was frightened of donkeys and did not want to go near them.
Clare was hungry and bought an ice cream with a female relative.
James and his big sister decided not to play beach games.
Mum had great fun playing beach games with her child.

	RELATIVE	TREAT
Lucy		
Clare		
James		
Jamila		

Puzzle

In the sets of words below, there is a word that links all the other words together. This word reads vertically down the lightly shaded column of each grid. The first one has been started for you. Place all the words into each grid and then read down the lightly shaded column to find your linking word.

	S	N	O	W	F	L	A	K	E

FLOWER   BATHROOM   BARGE   SEASIDE   SNOWFLAKE

1 The linking word is: _____

TEETH   DINNER   MUNCHING   ROAST   GRAVY   VEGETABLE

2 The linking word is: _____

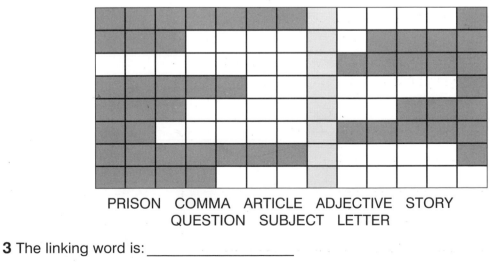

PRISON   COMMA   ARTICLE   ADJECTIVE   STORY
QUESTION   SUBJECT   LETTER

3 The linking word is: _____

Puzzle ⑤

Using the letters in the star, make as many words as you can. You must use the central letter every time and each letter only once. No two-letter words, initials or proper nouns are allowed. Good luck!

Example:

priest	strip	ripe	sir
sprite		tire	rip
		rest	

For a good score aim to get: 2 x 6-letter words
8 x 5-letter words
8 x 4-letter words at least!

6-letter words

_____
_____
_____
_____
_____
_____

5-letter words

_____ _____
_____ _____
_____ _____
_____ _____
_____ _____
_____ _____

4-letter words

_____ _____
_____ _____
_____ _____
_____ _____
_____ _____
_____ _____

3-letter words

_____ _____ _____
_____ _____ _____
_____ _____ _____
_____ _____ _____
_____ _____ _____
_____ _____ _____

Progress Grid

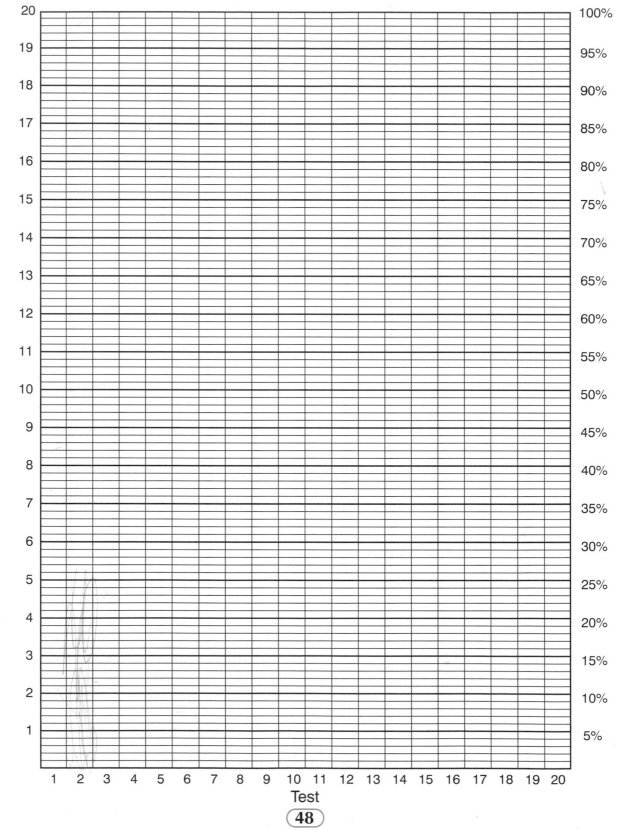

Total marks

Test